Karl
Jenkins

St Asaph's Dance

Solo harp &
optional tambourine

Boosey & Hawkes Music Publishers Ltd
www.boosey.com

ST ASAPH'S DANCE

KARL JENKINS
(b 1944)

19390

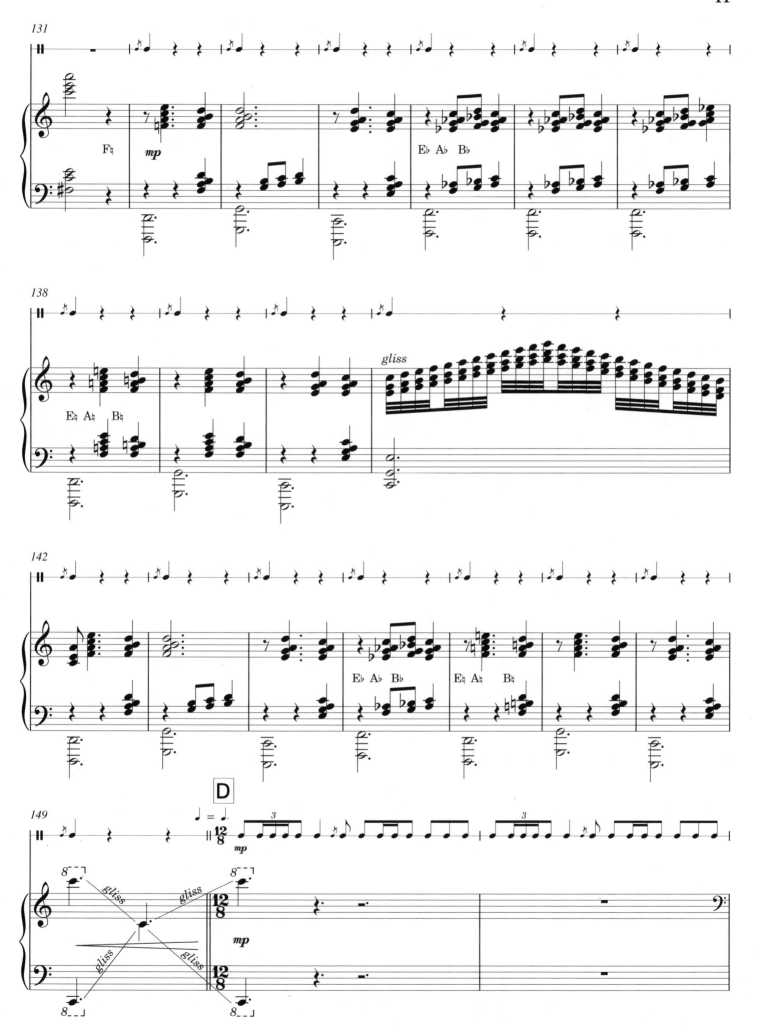

Commissioned by the North Wales International Music Festival,
to celebrate 40 years of magical music,
in conjunction with Festival friends and supporters, including:

Holywell Music Ltd
Ty Cerdd Music Centre Wales
Miss Heulwen M Ellis
Christopher Frost
Prof T J M Boyd
Dr Terry and Lindsay Crowther
Ann Atkinson and Kevin Sharp
Mr and Mrs D A Aiken
Mr and Mrs P Beaumont
Mair Dowell
Geoffrey and Patricia Hubbard
Mrs Patricia Palmer
Mr and Mrs J Solbe
Mr and Mrs D J Thomas
Prof John Last and Mrs Sue Last

Glyn and Nancy Davies
St Kentigern Guild
Anne Dennis
Mrs B C Eastland
Mr and Mrs Hodgkinson
Beryl Lloyd Roberts
Jennifer Lady Newborough
Mrs Gwyneth Peters
The Right Revd Dr Gregory K Cameron
Mr Ronald Davies
Robert and Andrea Ingham
Major and Mrs T Smith
Mrs Christine Ann Hancock
Mrs L Mathias
Mrs Y J McCormack

First performed by Hannah Stone on 23 September 2012
at St Asaph Cathedral, Denbighshire,
in the North Wales International Festival

Duration: 7 minutes

Optional tambourine part available as free download from www.boosey.com/StAsaphsDance/tambourine

Published by Boosey & Hawkes Music Publishers Ltd
Aldwych House
71–91 Aldwych
London
WC2B 4HN

www.boosey.com

AN IMAGEM COMPANY

ISMN 979-0-060-13095-3
ISBN 978-1-78454-161-3

First impression 2015

Printed by Halstan:
Halstan UK, 2–10 Plantation Road, Amersham, Bucks, HP6 6HJ. United Kingdom
Halstan DE, Weißliliengasse 4, 55116 Mainz. Germany

Music origination by Kottamester Bt, Budapest